What's the Wea[ther], Curious George?

Written by Francie Alexander

T0033758

Houghton Mifflin Harcourt
Boston   New York

George loves to play outside in all kinds of weather.

sunny

cloudy

rainy

snowy

What is the
weather today?
Is it sunny, cloudy,
rainy, or snowy?

Today is sunny.
George will wear his sunglasses.
He will have lots of fun.

George looks out the window.
What is the weather today?
It is cloudy.

The man tells George it
looks like rain.
What will George do?

George is ready to splash and play.
He is not stopped by a rainy day.

What is the weather today?
Hip, hip hooray!
It is a snowy day.

What will George do?
He makes a snowman!